Little Known Facts
About India

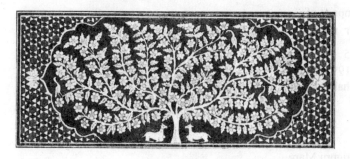

Swarn Khandpur

eESHWAR

e ESHWAR is an imprint of
BPI (INDIA) PVT LTD

ISBN 81-86982-20-5
©Swarn Khandpur, 1998
Illustrations by Prabhakar Wairkar

Published by

e ESHWAR
229/A Krantiveer Rajguru Marg
Girgaon Mumbai 400 004
Tel 380 88 17 / 19 Fax 387 2625
email bpipl@vsnl.com
website: http://www.bpipl.com

*P*anchavadyam, a variety of temple music of Kerela, produced by a combination of 5 different instruments, has gained so much popularity in the West that the performers are frequently invited to perform abroad. Some Westerners come to India specifically to learn it.

*A*dhai-din-ka-Jhonpra (a hut of two-and-a half days), is actually a ruined mosque near Ajmer. Its name is derived from the site where a fair used to be held for two-and-a-half days.

*A*kbar, the Great Mughal Emperor, never learnt to read or write. When the time for his formal initiation into schooling was fixed, Akbar did not show up for the ceremony. He was busy flying pigeons.

*T*he holy verses in Arabic inscribed above the central doorway of the Taj Mahal are written in such a way that all the letters appear to be of the same size when read from below. Actually the letters are graduated in size.

$\mathscr{A}$ll sun temples were constructed in such a way that the first rays of the rising sun fell on the idols. Temples to the Sun God were built between the 4th and the 13th century.

$\mathscr{T}$he Taj Mahal is so proportionately constructed, one can never imagine that it is taller than the Qutab Minar, the tallest minaret in the world! The Taj Mahal is 243½ ft. in height while the Qutab Minar is only 239 ft.

*T*he 1600-year-old, Iron Pillar in Delhi, is so firmly planted in the ground that a cannon ball fired at it by the invader Nadir Shah, in 1739, could not fell or damage it except for causing a small dent in its smooth surface.

*I*t is a form of tribal etiquette among the Muria boys of Madhya Pradesh to present a hand-made comb to the girl he admires and wishes to marry. If the girl wears the comb in her hair, it means that she has accepted the marriage proposal.

$\mathcal{B}$ahadur Shah, the last Mughal emperor, who was exiled to Burma (Myanmar) by the British after the failure of the War of Independence in 1857, was buried in distant Rangoon while the Burmese King, Thiban, was buried in India at Ratnagiri, on the western coast of India.

$\mathcal{N}$athuram Vinayak Godse was caught red-handed while assassinating Mahatma Gandhi. Nevertheless, it took five years to convict him for the act.

*L*ike the Great Wall of China, India too had a wall about 40 kms long, running up and down the Aravallis. It had 34 fortresses in it. It was built by Rana Kumbha of Mewar, to protect his kingdom from invaders.

*T*uticorin on the southern coast of Tamil Nadu, is nicknamed the Pearl Harbour of India because of the pearl-fishing practised here for centuries.

Sawai means 'one and a quarter'. Raja Jai Singh of Jaipur was presented with the title 'Sawai' by the Emperor Aurangzeb, to indicate that he was superior to other men. This is the story of how he got the title.

When Jai Singh of Amber ascended the throne in 1699 at the age of 13, he was obliged to go to Delhi to pay his respects to Aurangzeb. When Jai Singh's name was announced at the *darbar*, the Emperor rushed down from his throne, seized the young raja by his shoulders and shaking him roughly said, "Both your father and grandfather were traitors! What do you expect from me?"

Jai Singh calmly answered, "At the wedding ceremony the bridegroom holds one of the bride's hands in his own and pledges to look after her all his life. The emperor has held me with both hands. What more can I ask for?" The raja's wit took Aurangazeb by surprise.

"You are wiser than your ancestors," he said , smiling and relaxing his hold. "Yes, wiser even than most men. I give you the title 'Sawai'."

From then on Jai Singh was known as Sawai Jai Singh.

Sufiana Kalam, literally meaning 'decent pen', has nothing to do with calligraphy. It is a type of devotional music sung by groups in Kashmir.

*T*he Taj of the Desert, is not in fact, a mausoleum like the Taj Mahal at Agra, but a palace—Umaid Bhavan in Jodhpur, with 347 rooms. As the story goes, there was a severe drought in the 1920s. The kind-hearted Umaid Singh, tried to distribute food free to his starved subjects. But the proud Marwari peasants shunned all charity.

"Give us work", they said. In response, the great palace was built and provided work as a relief measure for the famished people.

*T*he musical instrument *Rabab*, which came to India from Afghanistan with Pathan and Afghan travellers, is the present-day

Sarod, modified by generations of the Khan family, of which Ustad Amjad Ali Khan, the world famous maestro, is a member.

*O*n the eve of her marriage, the bride-to-be from the Paliwal Joshi community of Rajasthan, rides around the town on horseback in a procession led by a band.

*T*he Irula tribals of Tamil Nadu catch snakes with the speed at which most people run away from them. With only a hook, they catch snakes and then skin them alive. They have been eking out a

living by selling snake skins for centuries. Nowadays their innate skill is used for milking venom from snakes. The venom is used in medicinal preparations.

A simple cotton tablecloth, the yarn for which was handspun by Mahatma Gandhi, was one of the wedding gifts received by Prince Philip and Princess Elizabeth (now Queen Elizabeth II), in 1947.

*C*hand Bibi, a widow of Ali Adil Shah, was acting as regent to her infant nephew when the Mughals invaded Ahmednagar in 1599.

Chand Bibi defended the fort bravely but when defeat became inevitable, she ordered all the gold in the treasury to be smelted and made into cannon balls.

On them she had the words engraved that whomsoever found the balls could keep them. The dismay of the Mughal troops, eagerly waiting to ransack the treasury, can well be imagined.

*N*ur Jehan would not have become Jehangir's queen, if a rich merchant had not picked her up on his way to Agra. She had been abandoned by her poverty-striken parents. She grew up as Mehrun-Nisa

in the Agra *harem*, where her beauty so captivated Jehangir that she became Nur Jehan Begum, 'Light of the World'.

*S*everal south Indian temples have singing stone pillars. The central part of such pillars is chiselled into 7 to 16 bars which produce distinct notes similar to that of a xylophone, if tapped with a wooden mallet. What is significant is that the different bars are part of the same pillar.

*W*omen aged between 10 and 50 years are not allowed to enter the temple of Ayyappa at Sabarimala, in Kerela, although the temple doors are open to everyone else, irrespective of caste or creed. Those who intend visiting, observe austerities for 41 days.

*M*ilkha Singh, the 'Flying Sikh', participated in 82 competitions and won 79 of them.

*T*he Hindola Mahal or 'Swinging Palace', in Mandu, is most unusual in design. From outside it looks like a sturdy fort with

peculiarly sloping side walls, creating an illusion that the entire structure is swaying.

A dacoit-fan of the actress Meena Kumari, once made her autograph his hand with his own knife. This happened during the outdoor shooting of the film *Pakeezah,* when the unit was stranded in a dacoit-infested area of Madhya Pradesh.

*M*athura, about 130 kms from Delhi, has the distinction of having produced the first carved images of Buddha about 2000

years ago. Till then Buddha was never represented in human form. Symbols such as a horse to indicate his renunciation of princely life; a tree for his enlightenment; a wheel for his first sermon and a *stupa* for his *nirvana,* were used instead to represent him.

The Jantar Mantar at Delhi has two pillars about 12 ft in height and 17 ft apart, which determine the shortest and longest days of the year. On December 21, the shortest day of the year, the southern pillar casts a shadow on the northern pillar, covering it entirely— starting from the base upwards. On June 21, the longest day of the year, no shadow falls on the northern pillar—absolutely ingenious.

At the Karnidevi Temple in Rajasthan, rats are worshipped as the deity's descendants. So much so that they are not even referred to as rats. They are called *kabas* instead, the Marwari word for children.

Although rats are numerous in the temple, sighting a white rat is considered very auspicious. Devotees return to the temple again and again, until they actually get to see one. The extent of the people's devotion is evident at prayer time. After the morning and evening *artis*, the rats rush to the plate filled with *prasad*. Only after the rats have eaten some of it, is the *prasad* offered to the devotees, who partake of it without any revulsion.

*H*ave you ever noticed that only the one rupee notes carry the words 'Government of India' while all other currency notes have the 'Reserve Bank of India' printed on them?

*T*he Portugese discovered a variety of plants in the New World which they brought along with them and eventually introduced to India. These include *batata* (potato), the *couve* (cabbage, which became *gobi* or *kobi*), tobacco, tomato, cashew, *ananas* (pineapple), papaya, *pera* (guava or *peru*). *Pao* (bread) and *biscoito* (biscuit) prepared in Portuguese bakeries became popular. Their introduction of green and red chillies revolutionised Indian cuisine.

*I*n the Nicobar islands, pigs are reared on coconuts.

*T*he Indian wild ass, called Khur, found only in the desert of the Rann of Kutch, runs faster than the horse. In fact, a relay of horses is needed to tire it out before it can be caught.

*D*espite its name, Keoladeo Ghana is not in Africa. It is a world-famous bird sanctuary at Bharatpur, Rajasthan. Keoladeo is the name of the ancient Shiva temple in the dense (*ghana*) forest which once used to cover the area.

A life-sized, rock-cut elephant stands at the site of the Kalinga war, with Emperor Ashoka's rock edicts inscribed in the Prakrit language, written in the Brahmi script. There is something special about these edicts — there is no mention of the Kalinga war (261 BC) in the edicts. The sculpted elephant signified Ashoka's conversion to Buddhism after his Kalinga victory.

*T*he quaint practice of *wasiqa* (endowment) which was started in the mid-18th century for the descendants of the Nawab of Lucknow, is still continued by the Government of India. Apart from those of royal lineage, descendants of the Nawab's many servants, also get *wasiqa*.

Moreover, on the death of a recipient, the children become *wasiqedars*. Today, among the 85 odd recipients, there are many who get a rupee and a few paise as their monthly endowment.

$\mathcal{D}$o you know that every year astronomers from all over India meet at the Jaipur Observatory and prepare the yearly *Panchang* (Indian almanac) with the help of various stone instruments built more than 250 years ago by Sawai Raja Jai Singh?

The Siddis of Gujarat, called *Habshis* by the locals, are descendants of certain African tribes. They were brought to India by Arab traders and sold to the Portuguese, the British and the local rulers, as domestic servants. Some of them rose to high positions because of their honesty and bravery. The ruler of Janjira was a Siddi. The Siddis speak a dialect of the Somali language.

On his visit to England in 1902 for the coronation of Edward VII, the Maharaja of Jaipur took with him in the ship, for drinking purposes, a six-month supply of Ganga water, as it is said to retain its freshness and purity for months on end.

*T*he priest at the famous Vishnu temple at Badrinath in the U.P. Himalayas, is always a *Nambudri brahmin* from Kerela. Badri is one of the four Hindu monastic *Mutts*—the other three are at Puri, Dwarka and Sringeri, established by Adi Shankara in the 8th century.

*T*he 400-year-old Jewish Town in Cochin has only 24 elderly Jews living there still—all the rest (30,000) have migrated to Israel (this was the figure in 1994).

*W*e salute the memory of a Muslim saint, Baba Buden, for the wonderful gift he gave to India—coffee. The saint arrived from Arabia and settled in the mountainous country of Chickmagalur in Karnataka, bringing with him a handful of coffee seeds which he planted for his own use. This was the beginning of coffee cultivation in India.

*B*elieve it or not, but India used to get its ice from the U.S.A.! The American speculators made *paise* (money) from *pani* (water), when they sent their first consignment of ice from Boston by ship to Calcutta in 1833. They sold it for two annas a seer (12½ paise a

kilo in modern times). So pleased was Governer General William Bentick, that he presented an inscribed silver cup to the crew.

*I*nspite of having the highest cattle population in the world, the Government of India intends importing dung from the Netherlands. It is believed to be environment-friendly. It is even named 'Envirodung'.

*D*o you know that the word 'rupee' was coined from the '*rupaiya*' of Sher Shah Sur, Sultan of Delhi (who drove out Humayun from India)? He had minted a coin in silver of 178 grams in 1542.

When the coin was given to him, he looked at it and exclaimed *"rupaiya"*, meaning 'beautiful'. It is a different matter that the present Indian rupee coin contains no silver—only copper and nickel.

*R*anjitsinhji, although acknowledged as the 'Father of Indian Cricket', after whom the national cricket championship (Ranji Trophy) is named, never in fact played for India! He had retired from cricket when India was given Test status in 1932.

*I*n this age of faxes and telexes, *harkaras* or mail runners could well be considered mythical creatures. In fact, 200 or so *dak harkaras* still exist, carrying mailbags in certain remote areas of Bihar, West Bengal and Kerela. Now no drummers or archers are needed, only the spear with its bell is enough to scare away the few animals that remain in the depleted forests through which the runners pass.

*U*nlike elsewhere in the country, the blowing of a conch does not augur festivity in the Uttarkhand region of Uttar Pradesh. On the contrary, it signifies that a death has occured in a neighbouring village and people should not only attend the last

rites but bring a contribution of a log or two for the cremation as well.

*F*ootball history was made in 1911, when a team of barefooted Indian players defeated an all-white team for the first time.

The Indians were playing for the Mohan Bagan Club which was established in Calcutta in 1889.

*P*ictures of gods and goddesses and scenes from the *Puranas*, which adorn the walls of millions of Hindu homes and work places, are imitations of paintings done by Ravi Verma, Raja of Kerela,

more than 100 years ago. So popular are these pictures that the Hindus visualise their god very much the way Ravi Verma depicted them in his paintings.

*T*he Great Imambara of Lucknow, a religious building where Moharrum is celebrated, has a intricate labyrinth of galleries and corridors called *Bhul Bhulaiyan*. The building was constructed during a great famine.

While work was carried out during the day, the same was demolished every night, by order of the Nawab, who thereby generated employment for his subjects in those trying times.

Emperor Shahjehan had built a screen made of gold around the tomb of Mumtaz in the Taj Mahal. It was later removed for fear of vandalism and replaced by a marble one with fine lattice work. But this too was sold by their son, Emperor Aurangzeb, to partly fund his innumerable military campaigns. The screen was replaced by another simpler one, carved with delicate patterns of leaves and flowers. This is still there for us to see.

To celebrate 100 years of Christianity in Mizoram, the faithful sang and danced to the beat of a huge drum—8 ft wide and 6 ft long,

which was specially chiselled out of the biggest tree in the state. Earlier, when the tree was felled, its trunk was found hollow and 10 tortoises came out of it.

$\mathscr{I}$f the Indian tiger is vanishing and fast becoming extinct, the number of lions is increasing in the country because lions proliferate rapidly. Gir Forest Sanctuary has forced the authorities to explore the possibility of finding a 'second home' for them in the country or to place them on birth-control pills.

*J*ute, which was traditionally used for making gunny bags, is now also blended with cotton, wool and even viscose. Jute-blended fabrics can be dyed, printed, as well as embroidered, and have become a boon for fashion designers.

*T*he East Indian Christians are not—as one might suppose—from the eastern, but the western coast of India. Converted to Christianity by the Portuguese at their original habitats around Salcette and Bassein, members of this community got their nomenclature from the East India Company, which gave them employment.

*K*odagu, which is now a district of Karnataka, was once an independent kingdom. The British who changed the name Kodagu to the Anglicised Coorg, feared the warlike Coorgis. Nevertheless, they allowed the Coorgis to carry arms without a licence—a privilege which they still enjoy.

*T*hough the exact number of people who speak, read or write English is not known, it is estimated that there are more English-speaking people in India than there are in Britain.

The Hindu, a major Indian newspaper, did not carry the news of Mahatma Gandhi's assasination on its front page—instead the page was full of advertisements, as per their policy.

*I*t is Ahmedabad and not Bombay which has the highest per capita consumption of ice-cream in India.

*S*ir Edmund Hillary and Tenzing Norgay deservedly received much praise when they were the first to climb to the summit of Mount Everest.

But how many people know that they had with them 12 climbers, 40 Sherpa guides and 700 porters?

*D*espite its claim to fame as the wettest place on earth, Mawsynram near Cherrapunjee in Meghalaya, has a terrible scarcity of drinking water. In the absence of proper water storage facilities, all the rain water drains down to Bangladesh.

*T*he remarkably beautiful 400-year-old Jewish synagogue, called the Pardeshi Synagogue, at Cochin, has delicate blue and white hand-painted tiles. No two tiles have the same design.

$\mathscr{B}$elieve it or not, *Kalnirnay* is India's largest selling publication. It is a Calmanac, that is, a calendar plus an almanac. It also has recipes, household hints and articles on various subjects—all rolled into one. Printed in 7 languages and also in Braille, *Kalnirnay* is a household name across the country.

$\mathscr{D}$o you know that in front of the well known *samadhi* of Chhatrapati Shivaji atop Raigad Fort, is a memorial to his pet dog, who is said to have jumped into the funeral pyre of his master and died?

$\mathscr{I}$f the Taj Mahal is unsurpassed in structural conception, the Jain Dilwara temples at Mount Abu are incomparable in detail and ornamentation. It is said that the carvers were paid in silver equal in weight to that of the marble filings.

$\mathscr{D}$evotees flock to the temple of Lord Venkateswara at Tirupati with offerings of gold, silver, cash and jewels, making the hill shrine one of the richest temples in the world. The *hundi* (a cloth container for offerings), which is emptied four to five times a day, bears deposits such as golden lotus flowers, gold biscuits, wads of currency

notes, solid gold *laddus* and innumerable coins of all denominations. Sieves are used to sort out the coins, which are weighed, being too numerous to count.

Once a huge quantity of smuggled gold was deposited into the *hundi*. While the customs officials wanted to confiscate it, the temple authorities considered it a donation. Finally, the matter was settled with the Lord paying a token fine of Rs 100 and keeping the booty.

*A*lthough Buddha himself never came to Sanchi in Madhya Pradesh, stories of his various births, called the *Jatakas*, are carved on elegant stone gateways which lead to the Great Stupa, dating as

far back as 2,000 years. Our ancients certainly found a unique way of telling stories.

The Mattancherry Palace in Cochin (Kerela), is erroneously referred to as the Dutch Palace. Built by the Portuguese and gifted to the then Raja of Cochin, the palace was later renovated by the Dutch, only to gain the misnomer of Dutch Palace.

*I*n the largest natural cave in the Himalayas, at a height of 12,729 ft., a Shiva *lingam* is formed of pure ice between July and August. How it happens—whether from the water dripping from the roof or by way of the frozen spring running underneath—is not known. But the *lingam* is said to wax and wane with the seasons or the phases of the moon. Despite the arduous journey, people throng in large numbers to Amarnath for a holy *darshan*.

A carved stone bracelet on a sculptered lady's wrist, can actually be moved back and forth in the Chennakeshava temple in Belur (Karnataka).

*A*bout 10 tonnes of roses are used to manufacture a kilo of *attar* which may cost a lakh of rupees! The sweet fragrance of pure *attar* lingers for 24 hours after it is applied because it is not alcohol-based.

*T*he *Tirthankaras* of the Jains, when shown seated in a cross-legged position, may look identical but can in fact, be distinguished by their mounts—a lion for Mahavira, a serpent for Parasvanatha, a bull for Adinatha and so on. These mounts are usually carved in the centre of the pedestals of the *Tirthankaras*.

One marvels at the carving skills of the ancients when one sees a 2 ft. high sculptured lady holding a jackfruit with a fly sitting on it and the wall lizard poised to attack—all carved in stone at the Chennakeshava temple in Belur (Karnataka).

Chidambaram, inTamil Nadu, is the only major temple where Lord Shiva is worshipped as Nataraja (Lord of Dance), instead of the usual *lingam*. It is also the only temple where the 108 dance postures described in the *Natya Shastra*, are carved.

The wide circular gallery running along the interior of the dome of the Gol Gumbaz at Bijapur, 100 ft. above the ground, is so ingeniously designed that the rustle of paper, the lighting of a matchstick, or even a whisper, is amplified and echoed. No wonder it is known as the Whispering Gallery.

The world famous Sun Temple at Konark, was designed as a celestial depiction of *Surya* the Sun God, who is believed to course across the sky in a chariot with 12 pairs of wheels, drawn by 7 horses. The 7 horses represent the 7 days of the week and each wheel represents one hour of the day.

*N*ear the famous temple of Somnath, which stands at the seashore in Saurashtra (Gujarat), is a pillar facing the Arabian Sea. This pillar is constructed on such a spot that no land comes between the pillar and the South Pole.

*T*he stepwell at Adalaj near Ahmedabad, resembles a subterranean temple. It descends 5 storeys underground, each storey having a pillared pavilion and a profusely carved gallery.

*I*n the tower of the famous Se Cathedral in Goa, which houses the holy relics of St. Francis Xavier, there is a bell which can be heard in Panjim, 14 kms away. And yet, when one stands next to the bell, its soft melodious tones fall lightly on the ear.

A huge boulder resting on a slender base, and known as Krishna's Butter Ball, fascinates visitors at Mahabalipuram (Tamil Nadu).
It is said, that even elephants cannot move it.

*A*lthough we follow the international Gregorian calendar for convenience, our national calendar, which is based on the Saka era, is 78 years behind the established Gregorian one.

*E*ver heard of a donkey *mela* ? Around Dussehra, a fair is held near Jaipur, when donkeys are brought and sold at prices ranging from Rs 100 to Rs 3000. Named after various famous film stars, donkeys form an important item of dowry in the potter's community.

*T*he *Chaumukha* (four-faced) shrine dedicated to Adinath, the first Jain *Tirthankar*, at Ranakpur in Rajasthan, consists of 84 halls with 1444 carved pillars, of which no two pillars are exactly alike. The pillars are placed in such a way that the view of the deity is not obstructed from any point.

*T*he world is a bridge, pass over it,
  but do not build upon it.
  The world endures but an hour,
  spend it in devotion.

Ironically, these are the words inscribed on the ancient Buland Darwaza at Fatehpur Sikri which Emperor Akbar built after conquering the kingdoms of the south.

*I*n the 7th century mosque at Kodungalloor in Kerela, *nilavilakus,* the traditional brass lamps of Hindu temples, are lighted daily.

*S*ri Venkateshwara, popularly known as Balaji, the Lord of the Seven Hills, has a staggering amount of personal wealth. There are

a total of 302 items of gold jewellery studded with gems, worth several crores. The ankle-length gold chain draped around the deity, donated by the erstwhile ruler of Mysore, is yet to be valued. There is also a fabulous diamond crown, valued at Rs 12 crore, one of the most valuable pieces of jewellery in the world.

$\mathcal{G}$ol Ghar, a 90-ft tall, inverted-bowl-like stucture, was built in 1788 as a granary in Patna. But it could not be used as such because the doors at the bottom, which opened inward, could not be opened when the granary was full.

$\mathcal{A}$ unique offering of human hair is made at the Tirupati temple. Men, women and children, young and old, rich and poor, offer their crowning glory as an act of surrendering their ego and vanity. Two special halls have rows of barbers for freecuts. Hair is usually offered as the fulfilment of a vow. The hair is collected, cleaned and sold in auction, fetching over Rs 4 crore a year!

$\mathcal{T}$he tombstone over Emperor Aurangzeb's open grave at Khuldabad near Aurangabad, eloquently reads thus:

No marble sheet should shield me from the sky
as I lie here one with the earth.

*E*very youngster in Darzeepara in Calcutta, is a tailor! These youngsters, about 15,000 in number, are in fact, descendants of tailor families that moved here in the 1850s, along with the Nawab of Oudh, who was exiled by the British.

*B*havnagar, in Gujarat, is the only railway station in India where women work as porters. This practice began when the local raja employed men to work at his palace and their wives were given licences as porters.

*I*n this age of telephones and fax, pigeons are still used as carriers of messages. The police in Cuttack (Orissa) maintain a loft of about 1000 pigeons and train them to carry messages to various police stations located in the hilly regions of the state.

The pigeon, with the message held in a tiny capsule tied to its leg, flies to its destination and also returns the same day with a reply.

*A*ppropriately called the *Rose Garden*, the Siachen glacier in the Karakoram Himalayas, has become the highest battlefield in the world—both India and Pakistan spend crores of rupees daily to keep the war effort going.

*K*achchh (Gujarat) is the only district in India where the cattle (40 lakh) outnumber humans (12.62 lakh).

*A*dolf Hitler's gift of a powerful telescope, to a Rana of Nepal, is now at Darjeeling (West Bengal), housed in the Himalayan Mountaineering Institute.

*O*n the full-moon day in April, one can see the spectacular sight of moonrise and sunset together, at Kanyakumari, on the southern-most tip of India, where the waters of the Arabian Sea, the Bay of Bengal and the Indian Ocean meet.

Clay for making Ganesh idols is transported all the way from Bhavnagar (Gujarat) to Pen in Maharashtra, about 700 kms away, where more than 2 lakh idols are made every year for the Ganesha festival.

The highest civilian award, the Bharat Ratna, given to the late Maulana Abdul Kalam Azad, was not bestowed at a glittering ceremony at the Rashtrapati Bhavan but was delivered by registered post to the Maulana's nephew in Calcutta.

In Assam, those who wish to do their doctorate (Ph.d) in Hindi, are nevertheless required to write their thesis in English.

*T*he Rambagh Palace, in Jaipur, was built especially so that Raja Ram Singh and his guests could play billiards in its several rooms undisturbed.

*T*he historic Qutab Minar does not cast a shadow on June 22 every year—a rare phenomenon because on other days, the minar casts a shadow even at noon due to its structural leaning.

*V*enom, which is extracted from poisonous snakes once every month, fetches prices varying from Rs 300 to Rs 3000 per gram—the venom of the krate fetches the highest price.

*S*hivaji, while under detention in the Agra fort, borrowed money through *hundi*, a kind of promissory note, an indigenous bill of exchange, still popular in many parts of India.

*T*he Todas of the Nilgiri hills calculate their ages by the blossoms of the *Kurinji*, a deep mauve flower which blossoms once in 12 years. The last time it blossomed was in 1992.

*A*lthough there are 16 different tribes living in Nagaland, to most of us, they are known simply as Nagas. Their distinctive

'shawls' differentiate one tribe from another, similar to the tartans worn by the Scots.

*T*he ice-skating rink in Shimla, Himachal Pradesh, is unique. It is prepared every year with the onset of the cold weather in November. After the ground is cleaned and levelled, water is sprayed to turn to frost overnight. This process of water-spraying is repeated till layers of frost turn into ice sufficiently hard for skating.

*I*t is forbidden to fly over the Taj Mahal in Agra, as the vibrations of aircraft can damage the structure.

A rare and unexplained phenomenon occurs between August 15 and October 31 on a cloudy, moonless night at Jatinga, near Haflong (Assam). Thousands of birds—little white egrets, hill patridges, pheasants, green pigeons, emerald doves and others—attracted to the lights of petromax lamps, come flying and get killed by people. The birds do not come if the wind is not blowing from south to north.

*T*he 4,000 ft.-long corridor of the Rameswaram Temple in south India, which has 985 richly carved pillars standing on both sides, presents a breath-taking perspective. The corridor, although the longest in the world, is not dark as light filters into it through occasional openings in the roof.

*T*he numerical 21 is associated with Lord Ganesha. Although he has many names, only 21 names are uttered while invoking him. And with each name one *modak* having 21 flutes is offered.

*J*ust before noon, two white kites come wheeling down out of the clear sky to the small shrine of Shiva on a hillock near Chennai. It is believed that these two birds are actually two saints who stop to rest and be fed by the temple priest, on their daily flight between the holy cities of Varanasi and Rameshwaram.

*S*ome people still prefer arranged marriages, but among the Garasia tribals of Rajasthan, it is customary to elope. This romantic but strange custom takes place during the full moon day of March-April, while the Gaur fair is in full swing. The girl's relatives

subsequently approach the *panchayat* to finalise the bride price payable to her father.

$\mathcal{T}$he icon of Lord Varaha Narasimha, the deity at the Simhachalam temple in Andhra Pradesh, is kept covered with kilos of sandal paste for 359 days a year. It is only on the third day of the first half of the month of Vaishaka (April-May), that the image of the Lord is seen in its original form.

*V*ijay Merchant, often called 'the master of scientific batting', hit only two sixers in his long career in first class cricket and that too, one off a no-ball. His radio programme *Cricket With Vijay Merchant,* was aired for 14 years continuously.

*O*live Ridley is not an Englishman but a species of sea-turtle, which comes to 'nest' at Gahirmatha beach in Orissa, all the way from across the Pacific Ocean, some 13,000 kms away. After laying their eggs, some 3,00,000 female-turtles go back, never to return to the 'nest' or to see their offspring hatch.

*T*he 6th Nizam of Hyderabad, Mir Mahbub Ali Khan, popularly known as Mahbub Ali Pasha, never wore the same clothes twice. His dressing room had the longest wardrobe in the world—a 240 ft-long corridor-like chamber lined with cupboards on both sides.

*T*he Sunehari Kothi, meaning a sparkling golden palace, located in Tonk near Jaipur in Rajasthan, has gold-inlaid walls and ceilings. It was built by Pindari chief Amir Khan, in 1824, when gold cost only Rs 15 a *tola* and workers were paid only 15 paise a day. Yet, the Sunehari Kothi cost Rs 10 lakh to build, even at that time.

$\mathcal{T}$he acoustics of the Golconda Fort near Hyderabad are unique because a handclap at the entrance of the fort can be clearly heard at the top-most pavilion, 400 ft above.

$\mathcal{B}$idriware, with its fine art of in-laying silver on a black metal surface, is famous the world over. But how many of us know that it is the mud from the walls of the old Bidar fort that turns the zinc-copper base of the article permanently black and brightens the silver at the same time? When and how the craftsmen discovered the alchemy or peculiar property of the mud, nobody knows, but one thing is certain—'without it there would be no Bidriware'.

*I*t was only in 1837 that an Englishman, James Princep, deciphered the script of the inscriptions engraved on pillars raised by Emperor Ashoka, 2000 years ago. Earlier, intrigued by the strange writing, Sultan Feroz Shah Tughlak (1351-1388), even offered a rich reward to scholars to decipher the writing but without success.

*O*nce the Siberian crane used to migrate to breed in the Bharatpur sanctuary in Rajasthan. Now their eggs are imported from Russia and hatched at Bharatpur.

The present Mahabodhi temple in Bodh Gaya is modelled after a temple design carved on a medallion found on the site. The original temple, built by Ashoka on the site where Gautama Siddhartha had attained enlightenment, was destroyed centuries ago.

Jojaba is a low, spreading bush which grows wild in Mexico. In the 1980's, the plant was introduced widely in Rajasthan and Gujarat to absorb salts in the local subsoil. The oil extracted from its leaves is used in perfumes. Now scientists have found a better use for it. Jojaba oil is the perfect substitute for whale oil used in missiles.

*A*cupuncture originated in India about 3,000 years ago but it was perfected in China. On the other hand, Homeopathy, though originating in Germany in the early 19th century, has almost 10 lakh practitioners in India today—more than anywhere else in the world.

*B*ismillah Khan, the great *shehnai* maestro, is the 'official' *shehnai* player at the famous Shiva temple of Vishwanath at Varanasi. He sits on a special, elevated platform to play to the Lord.

The Kailash temple at Ellora is carved out of a single hill. It was excavated without any mechanical aid by digging a 30 metre deep, three-sided trench from above, leaving the block of rock for the temple! Time and labour apparently did not count as obstacles, for it is said that about 20,000 tonnes of rock was chiselled out.

Have you ever heard of a 'temple transplant'? Well, in a unique salvage operation, 24 temples in the Mahboobnagar district of Andhra Pradesh were lifted, stone by stone, layer by layer, and reassembled at another site several kilometres away. This became

necessary to save the temples from inundation by the waters of the Srisailam Dam. This engineering feat is comparable to the 'lifting up' of the Abu Simbel shrines in Egypt, to save them from being swamped by Lake Nasser when the Aswan Dam was built.

$\mathcal{D}$een Dayal (1844-1905), became the first official photographer of the British in India, by chance—while portraying Vicereine Duffrein, he chanced to keep the lighting soft. As a result, her wrinkles did not show up—that won him her favour.

*T*he most imaginative monument dedicated to sport is the *Victory Bat* at Indore (Madhya Pradesh). It is a 30 ft. tall concrete cricket bat with Ajit Wadekar's signature carved on it, as well as the names of members of his team—in memory of their success in Britain, in 1971.

*T*he Mughals came to Srinagar (Kashmir) to beat the heat and laid out pleasure gardens. The British sought refuge from the great heat by introducing the tradition of houseboat living to circumvent the Maharaja's edict, prohibiting the ownership of land in Kashmir by non-Kashmiris and Europeans.

*T*he Kathiawari and Marwari horses are the only two pure Indian breeds. All other horses are either of foreign or mixed blood. The Marwari breed is found all over western Rajasthan, while the Kathiawari or (*Kathi*) is found only in Kathiawar (Gujarat).

*G*walior in Madhya Pradesh, was so advanced in music during the Mughal period that out of 36 musicians at Akbar's court, as many as 15 came from Gwalior. This fact finds mention in the *Ain-i-Akbari*.

Even at present, an average resident of Gwalior can easily distinguish one *rāga* from another, whatever his status. It has not been idly said, that when a child from Gwalior cries, it cries in a melodious tune!

$\mathcal{T}$he sacred fire which the Parsis had brought with them from Iran more than 1200 years ago, burns at Udwada, in Gujarat.

$\mathcal{T}$he 60 ft. tall staff of the Bijli Mahadev temple near Kulu in Himachal Pradesh, is reputed to be struck by lightning almost every year. The huge temple was built of large stones without the use of cement or mortar.

$\mathcal{T}$he metal mirrors of Kerela are unique. They are not made from glass but from tin and copper alloy. These mirrors provide

better reflection than the mirrors made from Belgium glass. The 500-year-old art now remains with only 4 members of a family in Aranmulla.

*T*he *Brahma Kamal,* known as the Bethlehem Lily in the West, blossoms only once a year in south India. The flower is large, pink or rose coloured and has a sweet lingering fragrance.

*G*olconda, near Hyderabad, is known today for its massive fort.

But how many know that it was the source of the Orloff, Regent, Hope, Great Mughal and Kohinoor diamonds? The last one is now part of the valuable British crown jewels.

*V*ernu, a village near Kachchh (Gujarat), has been in mourning for over 250 years, ever since its chief died while protecting the village from dacoits. The village people do not celebrate festivals; even marriage parties stop playing music once they enter the village.

*I*ndraprastha, Qila Rai Pithora, Siri, Tughlaqabad, Adilabad,

Ferozabad, Dinpanah, Shahjehanabad, these were some of the names by which Delhi was called at different times before it got its 9th name—New Delhi! Few cities in India can claim the long continuity and status that Delhi has enjoyed. No wonder it is a city with the largest number of historical monuments—more than 1000!

*M*ajuli, on the river Brahmaputra, in Assam, is the largest river island in the world, although the turbulent river threatens to wash it away ever year. Yet people continue to live there despite the prospect of such a calamity occuring.

$\mathcal{U}$jjain, known for its Mahakal Temple, which houses one of the 12 *Jyotirlingas* (manifestations of light), may also be called the 'Greenwich of ancient India'. The astronomers used the meridian passing through the *lingam* as the starting point for measuring longtitudes.

$\mathcal{I}$ron cased rockets, tied to bamboo poles, were first used by Tipu Sultan of Mysore against the British forces in 1780. These rockets had a range of about 3 kms. only. Thereafter, rockets became a part of the armoury of warfare.

*A*bade Faria, a Goan priest who discovered the art of hypnotism, is immortalised in the well-known classic of Alexandre Dumas, *Count de Monte Cristo*. The statue of this illustrious Goan stands in Panaji.

*I*n the Nasiyan Jain Temple in Ajmer, no flowers, no *prasad*, not even water, is offered to the *Tirthankar* in the belief that all these carry life. In fact, not even a *diya* is lit lest it attract moths. The Jain belief in the sanctity of life, forbids killing any living being, even an insect.

The rajas of princely states used to play Holi with *kumkums*—dainty mica balls filled with *gulal* (red colour). These *kumkums*, when thrown, would burst, splattering colour all round. *Kumkums* are now made of a dung and mud mixture!

The 5 *Shivalingas* worshipped for generations in the house of a Bangalore advocate, have turned out to be the world's 5 largest rubies. Purchased by his ancestors in the 16th century, during the Vijayanagar rule, these rubies now rest in a high security bank vault. Several offers have been made to buy them.

*S*trange though it may seem, the cricket stadium in Gwalior is named after a well-known hockey player, Roop Singh. This is because the ground was originally used for hockey.

*T*he Indian railways often run special trains to meet peculiar requirements. The 'Fish Therapy Special' is one such train, which runs annually from Guwahati to Hyderabad, for the benefit of asthma patients. The train is so named because at Hyderabad, as a medicine, the patient is made to swallow a live, medicated Murral fish. The railways even provide a special diet on-board to patients on their return journey.

*H*ow many of us know that India leads the world in the varieties of mango, which exceed 1000! For the lay person, a *langra* is a *langra,* but for the connoisseur, there is Langra Banarsi, Langra Hajipur, Langra Digha, Langra Hardoi, Langra Patna and so on. Mangoes are named after royalty, colour, flavour, taste, shape, precious stones, place and so forth.

eESHWAR

Author	Title	ISBN	Price
ALLEN/DWIVEDI	LIVES OF THE INDIAN PRINCES	81-86982-05-1	Rs. 325/-
BAGCHEE	NAD-UNDERSTANDING THE RAGA MUSIC - H.B	81-86982-08-6	Rs. 995/-
BAGCHEE	NAD-UNDERSTANDING THE RAGA MUSIC - P.B	81-86982-07-8	Rs. 395/-
BEDI	GODS AND GODDESSES OF INDIA	81-86982-04-3	Rs. 250/-
KHANDPUR	INDIA QUIZ	81-86982-13-2	Rs. 200/-
KAJI	YET ANOTHER BOOK ON VEDANTA	81-86982-55-8	Rs. 300/-
KRISHNAKUMAR	AGELESS GURU	81-86982-56-6	Rs. 200/-
KHANDPUR	LITTLE KNOWN FACTS ABOUT INDIA	81-86982-20-5	Rs. 55/-
MARATHE	TEMPLES OF INDIA	81-86982-11-6	Rs. 250/-
NAIR	THOUGHTS TO LIVE BY	81-86982-18-3	Rs. 200/-
NAIR	THOUGHTS TO MANAGE BY	81-86982-19-1	Rs. 250/-
PATIL	WHAT'S IN YOUR NAME? INDIAN BABY NAMES & THEIR ROOTS	81-86982-26-4	Rs. 300/-
RAGHUNANDAN	A SILENT JOURNEY	81-86982-95-7	Rs. 200/-
SINGH	FRUIT CHAAT	81-86982-33-7	Rs. 150/-
SHROFF	DOWN MEMORY LANE	81-86982-21-3	Rs. 200/-
THAKUR	PRIME MINISTER NEHRU TO VAJPAYEE	81-86982-72-8	Rs. 325/-
SHARMA	CURZON NAMA	81-86982-51-5	Rs. 295/-
BARIAN	ROAR OF THE GANGES	81-86982-87-6	Rs. 250/-
MAHADEVAN	MY TRYST WITH CANCER	81-86982-70-1	Rs. 150/-
SAWHNEY	NOTES FROM A FLUTE	81-86982-86-8	Rs. 125/-

NĒVĒ

Author	Title	ISBN	Price
	FAIRY TALES - (P.B)	81-86982-75-2	Rs. 120/-
	FAIRY TALES - (H.B)	81-86982-75-2	Rs. 160/-
	MY FIRST WORD BOOK	81-86982-65-5	Rs. 80/-
	MY FIRST DICTIONARY(P.B)	81-86982-64-7	Rs. 80/-
	MY FIRST DICTIONARY (H.B)	81-86982-64-7	Rs. 120/-
BASU	IT HAPPENED THAT YEAR	81-86982-54-X	Rs. 60/-
DWIVEDI	THE BROKEN FLUTE	81-86982-22-1	Rs. 60/-
GUPCHUP	FAMILY TIES (SET OF 8 VOLS)	81-86982-41-8	Rs. 100/-
GHOSE	THE BODHISATVA & THE GANG	81-86982-25-6	Rs. 100/-
GHOSE	GANG TALES FROM RANTHAMBHOR	81-86982-24-8	Rs. 100/-
BASU	UP TO THE NINES	81-7693-007-5	Rs. 75/-
DAS	LEGENDS OF INDIA'S TEMPLES	81-7693-024-5	Rs. 55/-
DAS	LEGENDS OF INDIA'S RIVERS	81-7693-016-4	Rs. 40/-
CUNHA	GOAN WHOOPEE	81-86982-96-5	Rs. 50/-
	BIBLE STORIES FOR CHILDREN	81-86982-76-0	Rs. 150/-
MARFATIA	DAYBOOK	81-7693-068-7	Rs. 295/-
PADMA T V	THE AMAZING ANIMAL KINGDOM (10 BOOKS)	81-7693-003-2	Rs. 30/-each

Zaika

Author	Title	ISBN	Price
BHATIA	FAVOURITE CHINESE DISHES	81-86982-06-X	Rs. 90/-
MARATHE	MAHARASHTRIAN CUISINE	81-86982-12-4	Rs. 125/-
BHATIA	FAVOURITE DISHES OF INDIA	81-86982-09-4	Rs. 125/-
PATIL	INTERNATIONAL FOOD INDIAN STYLE	81-86982-49-3	Rs. 100/-
VIJ	151 FISH TEMPTATIONS	81-86982-83-3	Rs. 100/-
VIJ	EGG FIESTA	81-86982-84-1	Rs. 100/-
VIJ	MUTTON MAGIC	81-86982-98-1	Rs. 100/-
VIJ	INDIAN BREAD BASKET	81-7693-000-8	Rs. 100/-
VIJ	CLASSIC CHINESE CUISINE	81-86982-06-X	Rs. 100/-

BUSINESS PUBLICATIONS

Author	Title	ISBN	Price
BRANDT	ENTREPRENEURING- BUILDING A GROWTH COMPANY	81-86982-60-4	Rs. 500/-
BRAITHWAITE	THE POWER OF IT	81-86982-01-9	Rs. 175/-
BALAN	PRODUCTIVITY IN THE AGE OF COMPETITIVENESS	81-86982-78-7	Rs. 250/-
BASU	THE CAN'T GO WRONG BOOK OF COCKTAILS	81-86982-30-2	Rs. 500/-
COLLIS	THE 7 FATAL MANAGEMENT SINS	81-86982-40-X	Rs. 595/-
DINKMEYER	LEADERSHIP BY ENCOURAGEMENT	81-86982-02-7	Rs. 195/-
GOPALAKRISHNAN	DICTIONARY OF ABBREVIATIONS	81-86982-27-2	Rs. 100/-
GOPALAKRISHNAN	GLOSSARY OF PLACES	81-86982-59-0	Rs. 125/-